READ WELL
FLUENCY FOUNDATIONS
Storybook
Units A-E

Fluency Foundations, Units A–E

8 9 10 11 12 13   DSG   15 14 13 12 11

ISBN 978-1-60218-514-2
ISBN 1-60218-514-X
166748/9-11

Printed in the United States of America
Published and Distributed by

Cambium
LEARNING®
Sopris West®

4093 Specialty Place • Longmont, CO 80504 • (303) 651-2829
www.voyagerlearning.com

TABLE OF CONTENTS
Storybook, Units A-E
FLUENCY FOUNDATIONS

Unit C
The New Bobcat

Unit D
Harriet Tubman Escapes

Freedom Fighter

Unit E
Little Brother Tuck

Unit A

The Song Contest

by Ann Watanabe
illustrated by Clark Tate

Chapter 1
The Big Event

It was time for the big Song Contest. The first contestant was Moose. This big mammal represented the herbivores, or plant-eating animals. It was time to begin.

Deer said, "Moose!"   3

Moose was near the stream with weeds in   11
his teeth. Swoosh! Moose ran to the trees. "I   20
can do this," he said. "Oo, oo! I am a moose."   31

What is the big event? What kind of animal is Moose?

Moose quickly swallowed his weeds and got ready to sing. He was confident—sure of himself. Moose stepped up to the microphone.

Seeds, seeds, seeds,
Treats to eat.
Weeds, weeds, weeds,
Snacks to eat.

Near the trees and stream
Are weeds and seeds to eat.
Smack, smack, smack,
Sweet treats to eat.

 said, "Hoot, hoot!"

Deer and said, "Sweet, sweet!"

The audience went wild. They applauded for a long time and then waited for the next contestant.

Why do you think Moose sang about weeds and seeds? How do you know he sang well?

Chapter 2
Lion Sings

Who was the first contestant in the Song Contest? Why did he sing about weeds and seeds?

The Song Contest continued. The next contestant was Lion. Lion represented the carnivores, or mostly meat-eating animals. A nervous Lion walked slowly up to the microphone and took a long slow bow.

"I wish would start soon,"

said Deer.

"Me too," said .

"Start," said . "Start."

What kind of animal is Lion? Why do you think he didn't start right away?

Lion looked at the audience. He took a deep breath.

"I can do this," said . "Ar, arrrrr.

I am a smart ."

M-E-A-T
I need to eat and eat.
M-E-A-T
I need to eat and eat.

Meat is a treat,
Meat, meat, meat.
I can't eat weeds and seeds,
I need meat, meat, meat!

"He is a star," said .

The audience stood up and cheered. Lion had impressed everyone with his great singing. The next contestant had a hard act to follow.

Why do you think Lion sang about meat? What tells you Lion did well?

Chapter 3
Song and Dance Routine

Who were the first two contestants? How did they do?

The Song Contest was almost over. The last contestant was Raccoon. Raccoon represented the omnivores, animals that eat both meat and plants. Raccoon would have to be extraordinary—especially good. The judges knew it would be hard to pick a winner.

"This is too hard," said Deer to [owl]   8

and [bear] . "Moose was sweet and   14

[lion] was a treat."   18

"What can Raccoon do?" said Deer.   24

"Raccoon can't win."   27

"We need to see," said [owl] .   33

What kind of animal is Raccoon? Why does Raccoon need to be *extraordinary* to win?

Raccoon skipped joyfully onto the stage wearing a black top hat, a bow tie, and shiny black shoes. He held a black cane in one hand and clutched some ham and some weeds in the other. He took a deep breath and went into a lively song and tap dance.

Can we eat? Can we eat?	6
Weeds and ham, weeds and ham.	12
Ham and weeds are sweet.	17
Weeds and ham are sweet.	22
Smack, smack, smack.	25
What a treat!	28

Raccoon had the audience and judges on their feet, tapping, clapping, and singing along. It was an extraordinary performance.

Why do you think Raccoon sang about weeds and ham? What made Raccoon's performance extraordinary? Who do you think is going to win the contest?

Chapter 4
The Winner

Who was the last contestant? Describe Raccoon's performance.

The Song Contest trophy was brought to the stage. For a long time, the judges had been trying to decide who was the winner. Finally, Deer stepped to the microphone. Everyone was silent.

Deer said, "This was hard. We want a 8

star. Moose was sweet. 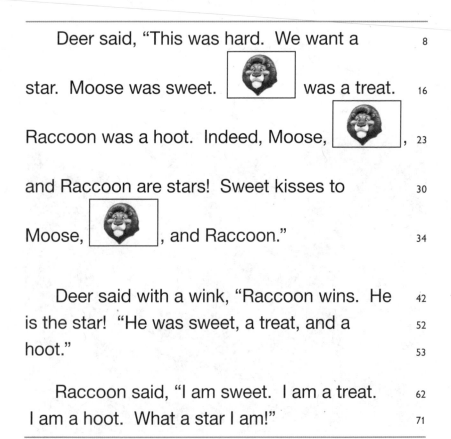 was a treat. 16

Raccoon was a hoot. Indeed, Moose, [ ], 23

and Raccoon are stars! Sweet kisses to 30

Moose, [ ], and Raccoon." 34

Deer said with a wink, "Raccoon wins. He 42
is the star! "He was sweet, a treat, and a 52
hoot." 53

Raccoon said, "I am sweet. I am a treat. 62
I am a hoot. What a star I am!" 71

The audience began throwing kisses to the three contestants. All three had done a great job.

Who won the contest? Explain why you agree or disagree with the decision.

Moose and Lion were the first to congratulate Raccoon. It was the best Song Contest ever.

Afterword: Moose, Lion, and Raccoon now have a famous band, The Main Street Mammals.

What tells you Moose and Lion were good sports?

Unit B

Aesop's Fables

retold by Marilyn Sprick
illustrated by Graham Franciose

The Cricket and the Ant

Chapter 1

On a hot summer night, a gentle breeze drifted through the dry grass. A lazy cricket sat in the dark, singing a song.

"Crick, crick, crick." 3

An ant was near. Cricket said to the ant, 12
"Sit and rest with me. See the moon and the 22
stars." 23

Ant said, "I can't do that. I need to work. 33
We ants need seeds, insect meat, and sweets 41
to eat. We need treats in the nest. We need 51
to work, work, work!" 55

"Work?" asked Cricket. "I can't work and 62
rest." Then Cricket said, "Tee hee. Tee hee." 70

Cricket continued, "There is plenty of food around. You are a foolish ant. There is food spilling from your tunnels. It's time to stop storing food. It's time to sing and play!"

Describe Cricket. Describe Ant. What's different about the two main characters? Which insect do you think is smarter? Why?

The Cricket and the Ant
Chapter 2

Who are the main characters? What time of year did Chapter 1 take place? What do you think will happen next?

Cricket had spent his summer days playing in the meadow while Ant worked hard storing food. Then winter came. A cold wind blew across the land. Snow covered the grass. Underground, Ant and her sisters had tunnels full of food to eat.

"Crick, crick, crick," said the sad cricket. 7
"I need to eat." Cricket sat near Ant's nest 16
and shed a tear. 20

Ant could hear Cricket cry. 25

"My, my, my," said Ant. "This is sad. 33
Cricket needs to eat. I can't stand to hear 42
him cry." 44

Then Ant went to Cricket with 10 seeds. 52

The sad cricket said, "Thanks, dear Ant. 59
Work is sweet." 62

"I will work when the grass is green. I will work when the sun is warm. I have learned my lesson."

What do you think Cricket means by "Work is sweet"? What lesson did Cricket learn? What did we learn?

The Hen and the Bucket

A little old hen needed a cool drink. She went to the well. The well was dry. "What will I do?" asked the hen. "I need a cool, cool drink." The hen was sad. She needed to think.

Just as the hen thought she might faint, she spotted a bucket. Rain water was at the bottom of the bucket, but the hen couldn't reach the water. The hen was sad until she had an idea. She would drop pebbles into the bucket to make the water rise.

The hen began picking up pebbles. She was determined to get a drink.

What is the hen's problem? What is her idea?

"There is a drink in that ," said the hen. "I can do this, I can. I will do this, I will."

Then the hen started to work. It was hard, hard work.

One, two, three! Work! Work! Work!

"I can do this, I can. I will do this, I will," said the hen.

It was hard, hard work.

At last, the hen said, "Look at that! I did it. I can drink. What a cool drink this is."

The hen drank and drank the cool water until she was no longer thirsty. The hen learned a lesson, and so did we.

What lesson did we learn?

The Cat and the Rat

A cat rested in a dark room. Sssss. A rat 10
was near the cat. 14

"Tee hee," said the rat. "Look at me." 22
Then the rat ran. 26

The cat said, "What's that? I think I hear 35
a rat. I think I smell a rat!" 43

"Ha!" said the sly cat. "This is his end. I 53
will eat that rat. I will!" 59

The cat placed his big paw on the rat's tail. The rat had been foolish to play games with the sly cat.

In great fear, the rat said, "Please let me go. Someday I will help you."

The cat laughed and laughed and let the rat go.

Then one day, the cat got caught in a trap.

In the dark room, the cat was sad. He started to cry.

"What's this?" asked the rat. "I hear the cat. He is sad. That cat needs me! I can work hard. I will work hard." And he did.

The rat got a stick. He worked hard and pried open the trap. Finally, the cat was free. From that day on, the little rat and the big cat were great friends.

How did the rat help the cat? What lesson did we learn?

Unit C

The New Bobcat

by Ann Watanabe
illustrated by Maurie J. Manning

Chapter 1

New Kid on the Block

What's the title of the chapter? What do you think this chapter will be about?

Rod had just moved. He was the new kid on the block. He missed his friends and wished he could be back in his old neighborhood, where he was the star of the baseball team.

Who is the story about? What is his problem?

Rod sat in his room with his little dog, Kit. 10

"I wish I could see my team," Rod said. 19

Kit and Rod seemed sad. 24

Rod said, "I miss the Sharks. The Sharks 32
are cool. The Sharks are my team." 39

Rod's mom said, "I signed you up for the neighborhood baseball team. You can make new friends with the Bobcats."

A *mood* is how you feel. Is Rod in a happy or sad mood? Why? Rod's mom is trying to make him feel better. What did she do? Who are the Bobcats?

Mom could see that Rod was in a sad mood.

Mom said, "I met the team. I think they are cool. Let's meet them at the sandlot."

Rod said, "I want to see the Sharks. I do not want to meet the team."

What does Rod want to do? What do you think will happen next?

Chapter 2
Meet the Team

Who is the story about? What is his problem? What do you think will happen next?

Rod was the new kid on the block. He missed his old baseball team, but Rod's mom had signed him up to play for the Bobcats. Rod gathered his baseball equipment and got ready to meet the team.

Rod and Mom went to meet the team. 8

Rod said, "I do not want to be a Bobcat." 18

At the sandlot, Rod could hear the team: 26

We are the Bobcats, 30
the Tenth Street Bobcats! 34

Rod met Bill, Matt, Bob, Ann, and Beth. 42
"I can hit the ball hard!" said Beth. 50

"I can too," said Rod. 55

"Want to hit the ball?" asked Beth. 62

What did Beth ask? How do you think that made Rod feel?

As Beth spoke out loud, she also talked in sign language with her hands. Rod signed back. Beth was excited! Rod had learned American Sign Language at his old school.

Why do you think Beth talked with her hands? Yes, Beth is deaf. What does Rod know how to do? Why did Rod know how to sign?

What do you think will happen next?

Chapter 3

Bobcat Rod

Who is the story about? What was his problem? What happened when Rod met the Bobcats?

It was Rod's second day of practice with his new team. Even though he still missed his old teammates, he was excited about his new team and the new friends he had made.

"Mom, the team is cool!" said Rod. "Beth and Matt can hit hard."   8   13

"I am glad the team is cool," said Mom. "Get the bat and mitt. We need to go."   22   31

Rod ran with the team. Dash! Rod was fast. Rod hit with the team. Whack! Rod could hit the ball hard. He hit the ball into the trees.   39   47   57   59

Beth said, "I'm glad that Rod is a Bobcat. He can hit far!"   68   72

Rod had a big, big grin.   78

Is Rod still in a sad mood? How can you tell? How does he feel about the new team? Why?

Chapter 4

A Big Hit

Who is Rod? Who are the Bobcats? What do you think will happen in this chapter?

Rod and the Bobcats won many games. Finally, it was the day of the big game. The winner would go to the playoffs. In the last inning, the score was tied.

Rod was at bat. Whoosh! He could not 8
hit the ball. 11

"Let Beth hit," said Ann. "She is the star." 20

Rod was still at bat. Whoosh! Rod could 28
not hit the ball. 32

"Let Beth hit," said Matt. "She will smack 40
that ball!" 42

"No," said Beth. "We are a team. Rod is a 52
Bobcat. Rod can hit the ball. Let him try." 61

Whack! Rod hit the ball into the trees. It 70
was a grand slam! 74

The Bobcats said:

We are a team. We try, try, try.
See that ball fly, fly, fly!

At the beginning of the chapter, Rod had a problem. What was it? How did Beth help him? Who won the game? Why? Did you like the story? Why or why not?

Unit D

Harriet Tubman Escapes

by Karen Akiyama-Paik
illustrated by Liz Wolf

Chapter 1
Harriet's Dream

What's the title of the chapter?

Around 300 years ago, thousands of people were stolen from their homes in Africa. Many were brought to America to be sold as slaves. A slave is someone who is owned by another person. This is wrong. Today, slavery is illegal in the United States.

Harriet Tubman was born a slave long ago. She is an important person in the history of the United States.

Who is the story about? What do you know about her?

When Harriet was little, she had to work   8
hard. She had to scrub and dust and could   17
not rest. If she rested, she was hit.   25

Harriet said, "I am strong. I want to work   34
with the men." She worked hard, but she   42
wanted to be free.   46

Harriet cut logs and worked in the sun. She looked at the sky and dreamed of freedom. Some white people freed their slaves, but Harriet feared she would never be free unless she ran away.

When Harriet was little, she was a *slave*. Did Harriet like being a slave? What did she want? What did she think she needed to do?

Harriet sang as she cut logs in the sun with the men. The sky and wind let Harriet feel free.

She sang, "Let us go. Let us be free."

Could Harriet be free? Could she run to freedom?

Harriet said, "I need to be free. I must try."

What did Harriet want? Did Harriet's owner give her freedom? What did Harriet decide she would need to do to be free?

Chapter 2
Follow That Star

Who is the story about? What did Harriet want? What would she need to do to get what she wanted?

Harriet Tubman was a slave, but she wanted to be free. One night, Harriet ran away from her owner. Her father told her to follow the North Star. He told her to follow the moss that grows on the north side of the trees.

Harriet looked for the star. She ran far 8
to be free. She looked for the moss on the 18
trees. She ran farther and farther. 24

Harriet ran until she was free! At last, she 33
could do what she wanted. 38

After Harriet was free, she worked hard to 46
free her friends. Harriet took her friends from 54
farm to farm. She hid them in the dark. They 64
ran to be free. 68

Harriet and her friends sang, "Free at last! 76
Free at last!" 79

How did Harriet get her freedom? How did Harriet help others? What did Harriet and her friends sing?

Harriet Tubman was brave. She worked hard for what she believed was right. She helped more than 300 people escape to freedom.

Why is Harriet Tubman an important person in *history*?

Unit D

Freedom Fighter

by Karen Akiyama-Paik
illustrated by Liz Wolf

Chapter 1

Young Martin Luther King Jr.

Have you ever heard of Martin Luther King? What do you know about him?

Since the days of Harriet Tubman, many people have worked to make the United States a better place for all people. Martin Luther King Jr. was a minister who wanted all people to be treated with fairness. When he was a boy, he saw signs in many places that said, "Whites Only." He wanted this to change so all people would be treated the same.

When Martin was little, he could read. He said, "I can read the words. Why can't we eat or drink there?"   8   18   21

Martin's mother said, "It is because we are black."   28   30

Martin was smart, but he did not understand why he couldn't eat and drink where he wanted. Until he could do what he wanted, he would not be free.   37   44   53   59

Martin Luther King wanted all men and women to be free. He wanted all men and women to be treated well.   66   75   80

What did Martin Luther King Jr. think was unfair? What did Martin Luther King want for all people?

Chapter 2
A Dream of Freedom

Martin Luther King Jr. was a great leader who wanted all people to be treated equally. He believed in solving problems in peaceful ways. Martin got others to stop eating where black people were not allowed. He got others to stop riding buses that would not allow black people to sit where they wished. Martin and other people worked to change unfair laws.

What did Martin Luther King want? What was his dream?

Martin Luther King and his friends went to   8
eat where blacks were not wanted. The men   16
said, "Go!" Martin and his friends were not   24
treated well.   26

Martin wanted all men and women, black   33
or not, to be treated well. Martin and others   42
did not eat where blacks were not wanted.   50

Martin said, "Until we can sit where we   58
want on a bus, we cannot be free." Martin   67
and others did not go on buses.   74

When others got mad, Martin did not   81
grumble. Martin and his friends sang songs.   88

What was unfair? What did Martin and his friends try to change?

Others listened to Martin, but then he was   8
shot. We lost a great man. We remember   16
Martin Luther King because he dreamed that   23
all men and women would be treated well.   31

Let freedom ring!   34

Martin Luther King's dreams live on today. His work made life better for all people in America. He is an important person in history.

Why is Martin Luther King an important person in history who people still talk about?

Little Brother Tuck

by Ann Watanabe
illustrated by Kathryn Mitter

Chapter 1

Yuck! Yuck! Yuck!

What's the title of the chapter?

It had been almost a year since Tucker was adopted into Pip's family. At first, Pip wanted a sister, not a brother. When Tucker first arrived, Pip wrote this poem in her journal.

Yuck! Yuck! Yuck!   3
See my little brother Tuck.   8
He can coo. He can goo.   14
What's a sister to do?   19

Yuck! Yuck! Yuck!   22
See my little brother Tuck.   27
He's a bundle of muck.   32
My little brother Tuck.   36

Yuck! Yuck! Yuck!   39
See my little brother Tuck.   44
Scat, scat, boom, boom.   48
Get away from my room.   53

Pip wrote a funny poem. When Tuck first was *adopted*, how did Pip feel about having a baby brother? Was she in a good mood or a bad mood?

Now that a year had passed, Pip thought, "I'm glad I have a brother, not a sister." Just then, Tucker toddled into Pip's room. Soon it would be time for his birthday party—his first birthday party.

Pip said, "I'm glad you are my brother, Tuck! Sit with me. I will read to you." 8 17

Tucker sat on Pip's lap. Pip started to read a book about raccoons. 25 30

Mom popped into Pip's room. She said, "We need snacks for Tuck's one-year birthday party! Let's go to the market." 36 44 51

How does Pip feel about Tuck now? How do you know Pip is glad to have Tuck for her brother? What will happen next?

Chapter 2
To Market, To Market

Who is the story about? Where are Pip, Tuck, and Mom going?

Tuck's first birthday was coming soon. Mom, Pip, and Tuck were on their way to buy treats for Tuck's birthday party.

"We need food for Tuck's one-year   7
birthday party," said Mom. "So let's go to   15
the market."   17

Why are Pip, Tuck, and Mom going to the store? How old will Tucker be on his birthday?

Big sister Pip and little brother Tuck 7
got in the car. Off they went! "Go, go, 16
go," said Tuck. 19

"Let's sing Grandmother Bertha's 23
song," said Pip. 26

This little pig went to market. 32
This little pig was strong. 37
This little pig had a hot dog. 44
This little pig sang songs. 49
And this little pig said, 54
"Tee hee, tee hee, tee hee," 60
All day long. 63

Grandmother Bertha's song was fun. 68

Whose idea was it to sing? Why do you think Pip thought it was a good idea to sing? Does Pip enjoy her little brother? How can you tell?

Chapter 3
At the Market

Who is the story about? What are Pip, Tuck, and Mom doing?

Now that Tuck was one year old, Pip thought it was fun to shop with Mom and Tuck.

Tuck was in the shopping cart.   6

"Peek-a-boo. I see you." Pip played with   15
Tuck in the shopping cart. Tuck grinned and   23
grinned.   24

Why did Tuck grin and grin?

Mom and Pip started to look for food for the party. Mom had a long list.

1. hot dogs and buns
2. crab and clams
3. drinks
4. cups, spoons, napkins
5. hats

Tuck said, "Book, book." 37

Pip's mother picked up the book. "This is 45 a fun book. Let's get it for Tuck," she said. 55

Look at the grocery list. What is on the list for Tuck's first birthday party? What else do you think they will have at the party?

Chapter 4
Tuck's Birthday Party

What do you think this chapter will be about?

People started to arrive at the house. Pip bragged about Tucker to everyone.

She said, "We adopted Tucker one year 7
ago. I remember being upset and saying, 14
'Send my brother back!' I am glad we did not 24
send him back. Tucker is the best!" 31

How long has Tucker been Pip's brother? How does Pip feel about her brother now?

Soon the birthday party started. 36
Grandmother Bertha handed Tucker a gift. 42
Pip's best friend, Peg, handed Tucker a gift 50
too. Tucker got a truck and a book. He got 60
blocks and a pet fish. 65

Mom and Dad said, "Pip, you are the best 74
sister. You read to Tuck. You pick him up 83
when he is crying. We are glad you are his 93
sister. This is your party too." 99

What did Tuck get for his birthday? Why do Mom and Dad think that Pip is the best sister? I liked this story because Pip and Tuck have fun together. Did you like the story? Why or why not?